THESE MEMORIES
HOARDED BY:

_____

The Memory Hoarder's Journal

FOR PEOPLE WHO WANT TO REMEMBER EVERYTHING

by Jason Shapiro

KNOCK KNOCK®

VENICE, CALIFORNIA

Created, published, and distributed by Knock Knock
1635-B Electric Ave.
Venice, CA 90291
knockknockstuff.com
Knock Knock is a registered trademark of Knock Knock LLC

Images used under license from:
iStock.com:
5: jim pruitt; 29: spxChrome; 30: WendellandCarolyn; 82: Jesus Jauregui; 84: qbanczyk;
85: Issaurinko

Shutterstock.com:
Cover: Aekawit Rammaket; 1: Sensay; 2: lynea; 6: Everett Collection; 18: panyajampatong;
22: Smith1972; 25: Nattawat Kaewjirasit; 27: Pixel Memoirs; 28: GoodMood Photo; 31: Everett
Collection; 42: Margo Harrison; 45: Khalchenko Alina; 46: Florin Burlan; 50: Ensuper;
52: CHOATphotographer; 53: Andrey_Popov; 62: Annette Shaff; 69: Big Pants Production;
75: Who is Danny; 79: Aaron Amat; 85: Mehmet Cetin; 86: Everett Collection; 88: liewluck

Unsplash.com:
47: Alisa Anton; 78: Stephanie McCabe; 91: Alessandro Pellacini Benassi

ISBN: 978-160106979-5
UPC: 825703-50152-0

10 9 8 7 6 5 4 3 2 1

Introduction

SOME PEOPLE MAY NOT THINK IT'S IMPORTANT TO REMEMBER THE PRICE OF POTATO SALAD ON A PARTICULAR DAY, OR THE BALANCE OF A STRANGER'S BANK ACCOUNT, BUT THOSE PEOPLE WILL NEVER KNOW TRUE PEACE OF MIND. THAT'S VERY SAD FOR THEM.

YOU WILL NEVER HAVE TO EXPERIENCE THAT SADNESS BECAUSE YOU ARE ABOUT TO START WRITING EVERYTHING DOWN. EVERYTHING. ALL THE TIME. THAT WAY, YOU'LL NEVER FORGET ANYTHING EVER AGAIN AND YOU CAN LIVE A TRULY HAPPY AND FULFILLED LIFE.

THIS JOURNAL COLLECTS ALL THE WONDERFUL MINUTIAE THAT SOME PEOPLE WOULDN'T FEEL THE NEED TO REMEMBER, BUT ABOVE ALL, IT'S A JOURNAL. SO WRITE DOWN WHATEVER YOU'D LIKE.

WORK THROUGH THIS JOURNAL IN ANY WAY THAT'S BEST FOR YOU; GO PAGE BY PAGE, SKIP AROUND, WHATEVER BRINGS YOU THE MOST INNER PEACE. JUST DON'T LOSE IT. KEEP IT IN A SAFE SPOT. PREFERABLY THE SAME SPOT, SO THAT YOU'LL ALWAYS KNOW WHERE IT IS.

WAVE GOODBYE TO FORGETFULNESS AND SAY HELLO TO PURE MEMORY BLISS.

YOU'RE WELCOME.

—— No. 1 ——
List of things
I'm worried that
I will forget:

1.

2.

3.

4.

5.

6.

7.

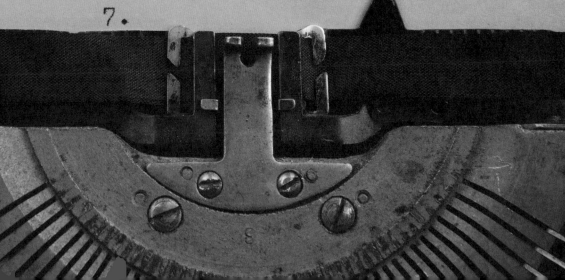

No. 2

Past vacation itinerary:

LOCATION:

DAY 3

EARLY MORNING:

MORNING:

NOON:

LUNCH:

AFTERNOON:

EARLY EVENING:

DINNER:

NIGHT:

LATE NIGHT:

No. 3

Paste a mail offer or coupon here:

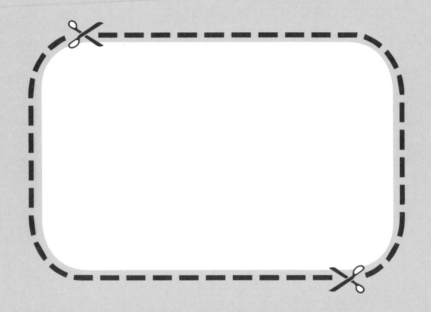

NEW STAMP DESIGNS I NOTICED:

OTHER THINGS TO SAVE
FROM THE MAIL:

MAIL I GOT THAT WASN'T MEANT
FOR ME BUT I STILL OPENED:

=== No.4 ===

Description of an interesting weirdo I saw:

WHAT THIS WEIRDO WAS WEARING:

WHAT I IMAGINE THE WEIRDO'S NAME IS:

PLEASANTRIES WE SHARED OR PLEASANTRIES
THAT I IMAGINED WE COULD HAVE SHARED:

U.S. states I've at least flown over

(CIRCLE ALL THAT APPLY)

Everything is worth remembering.

No. 6

Something I recently heard a stranger say:

"

"

THINGS I'VE RECENTLY
SAID TO STRANGERS:

THINGS I'VE RECENTLY SAID TO
STRANGERS UNDER MY BREATH:

No.7

Subject lines from emails currently in my spam folder:

☑ ☆ ▷   Loreta P.   You won $50,000   Claim   your prize   now!   11:51 pm

☐ ☆ ▶

☐ ☆ ▷

☐ ☆ ▷

☐ ☆ ▷

☐ ☆ ▷

☐ ☆ ▷

☐ ☆ ▷

☐ ☆ ▷

☐ ☆ ▷

☐ ☆ ▷

☐ ☆ ▷

☐ ☆ ▷

No. 8

Highlights of my most recent grocery store trip:

_____

_____

_____

PRICE OF MILK:

$_____

**PRICE OF CRACKERS
(THE EXPENSIVE KIND):**

$_____

**PRICE OF COOKING
MAGAZINE WITH SASSY
SENIORS ON THE COVER:**

$_____

No.9

Sixteen things I'm going to remember about today:

1.
2.
3.
4.
5.
6.
7.
8.

9.
10.
11.
12.
13.
14.
15.
16.

SIXTEEN THINGS I MIGHT HAVE FORGOTTEN SO FAR:

1.
2.
3.
4.
5.
6.
7.
8.

9.
10.
11.
12.
13.
14.
15.
16.

No. 10

Lyrics I know I'm singing wrong and should look up:

LYRICS I KNOW I'M SINGING WRONG BUT MINE ARE BETTER:

=== No.11 ===

Place deli number tickets here:

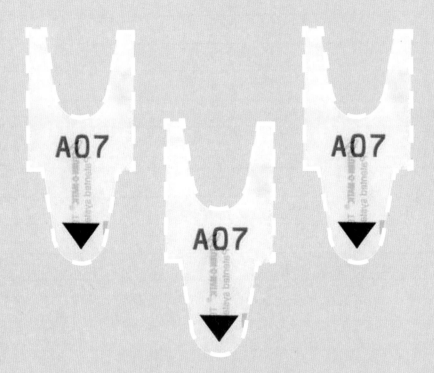

TYPES OF MEAT I NOTICED
FOR THE FIRST TIME:

_____

_____

_____

_____

PRICE OF POTATO SALAD: $_____

STRANGEST SALAD YET:

_____

_____

_____

No.12

Place found lists
I can't bear to
part with here:

Living in the moment

TIME ___:___ A.M. / P.M.

I AM:

☐ HOME   ☐ AT WORK   ☐ NOWHERE   ☐ OUTSIDE OF TIME AND SPACE

CURRENT THOUGHT 1:

CURRENT THOUGHT 2:

CURRENT THOUGHT 3:

No.13

Things I noticed on the ground while walking:

_____

_____

_____

_____

_____

_____

_____

_____

_____

_____

_____

_____

_____

_____

_____

WHAT I TOLD MYSELF TO JUSTIFY LEAVING THEM THERE:

_____

_____

_____

_____

No.14

All the teenage memories that I can think of at the moment:

No.15

Sharp things I've seen
and successfully avoided:

_____
_____
_____
_____
_____
_____
_____
_____
_____
_____
_____
_____
_____
_____
_____
_____
_____
_____

SHARP THINGS I DID NOT SUCCESSFULLY AVOID:_____

_____
_____

No. 16

Text messages
I got today:

(CIRCLE ALL THAT APPLY)

Call you back soon

K

Cool

Hey 😃

Hey 😉

U up?

Wut up?

?!

Hey

Word

...

NUMBER OF PHONE CALLS I GOT TODAY:

0 1 2 3 4 5 6 7 8 9 10+

REV 09/20

DATE:

No.17

Paste used airline baggage tags here:

08-4

0-45-9

0 123456 789012

DAC

0034567

Passenger's Signature
Final Destination

Airline	Flight	Zone
Via		

Airline	Flight	Zone
Via		

Airline

No. 18

Quotes to remember from things I saw on TV:

Living in the moment

CURRENT TIME: ___:___ A.M. / P.M.

CURRENT TEMPERATURE:

CURRENT MOOD:

CURRENT THOUGHT:

CURRENT MAYOR OF THE CITY I'M IN:

Constantly ask friends
and family to verify
your memories to make
sure you're getting
them right.

Paste pages from instruction manuals for appliances I no longer own here:

Handset

⑭ [MENU]
⑮ [OFF]
⑯ [PAUSE] [REDIAL]
⑰ [HOLD] [INTERCOM]

Note:
- Some operations not mentioned above are displayed as soft key selections during operation (page 17)
  Example: [Mute]

Using the navigator key

The handset navigator key can be used to navigate through menus and to select items shown on the display. by pressing [▲] [▼] [◄] or [►]

Adjusting audio volume

Press [▲] or [▼] repeatedly while talking

[▲]

[◄]   [►]

[▼]

❶ Speaker
❷ Soft keys
❸ Headset jack
❹ [☎] (TALK)
❺ Navigator key ([▲] [▼] [◄] [►])
❻ [⊜] (SP-PHONE)
❼ [✻] (TONE)
❽ [FLASH] [CALL WAIT]
❾ Microphone
❿ Charge contacts
⑪ Ringer indicator
   Message indicator
⑫ Receiver
⑬ Display

No.20

Past conversations I recalled while bored at work today:

No. 21

Place pennies here:

(LUCKY OR OTHERWISE)

STORY BEHIND ONE OF THESE PENNIES:

_____
_____
_____
_____
_____
_____
_____
_____
_____
_____
_____
_____

No.22

A billboard I noticed:

CIRCLE ONE:

WHILE DRIVING / WHILE WALKING / WHILE BIKING / OTHER

NO.23

Names of dogs I saw today:

(EITHER HEARD OR IMAGINED)

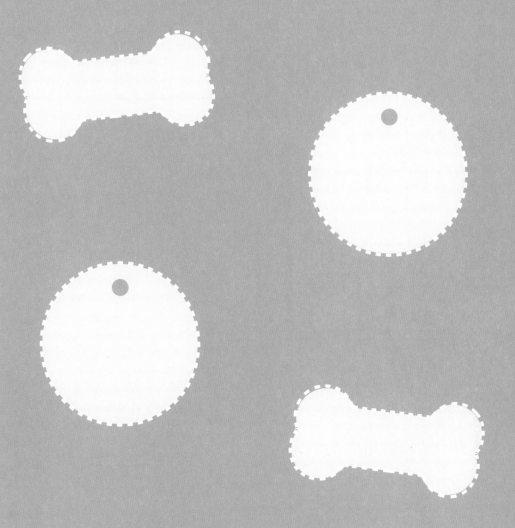

NUMBER OF DOGS I SAW TODAY:

0 1 2 3 4 5 6 7 8 9 10+

No.24

Odd things that have turned me on recently:

No.25

Gym locker combinations from my past:

DESCRIPTIONS OF PEOPLE THAT I ALWAYS USED TO SEE AT THE GYM:

THEIR NAMES AND OCCUPATIONS (REAL OR IMAGINED):

THEIR BIGGEST FEARS (REAL OR IMAGINED):

No.26

Important numbers in my phone that I still want to write down:

Name	☎

DATE:

Place impressive chunk of dryer lint here:

OBSERVATIONS:

_____

_____

_____

_____

_____

No. 28

Old clothing items
I need to track down:

- ☐ _____
- ☐ _____
- ☐ _____
- ☐ _____
- ☐ _____
- ☐ _____
- ☐ _____
- ☐ _____
- ☐ _____
- ☐ _____
- ☐ _____
- ☐ _____
- ☐ _____

No.29

Notes I remember from my high school yearbook:

NOTES I WROTE IN OTHER PEOPLE'S YEARBOOKS:

No. 30

Place fortune cookie fortune here:

PLACE FRIENDS' DISCARDED FORTUNE COOKIE FORTUNES HERE:

No. 31

Quotes I made up:

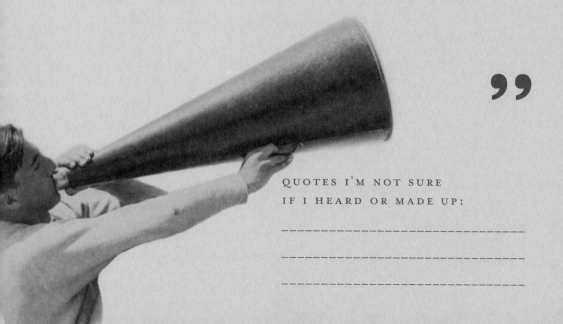

"

"

QUOTES I'M NOT SURE
IF I HEARD OR MADE UP:

_____

_____

_____

No. 32

Compliments I meant
to say to friends:

(BUT LEFT UNSAID)

No. 33

This week's winning lottery numbers:

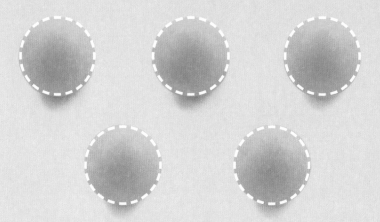

PLACE LOSING LOTTERY TICKET HERE IF APPLICABLE:

LOTTERY WINNER'S NAME AND LOCATION: _____
_____

No. 34

Cloud shapes I've recently seen:

PEOPLE'S FACES I OFTEN
SEE IN THE CLOUDS:

_____

_____

_____

_____

CLOUD SHAPES I SAW THAT
INSTANTLY EMBARRASSED ME:

_____

_____

_____

_____

No.35

Witty things I've said that I'm proud of:

THINGS I SHOULD NEVER SAY AGAIN:

No. 36

Place dry cleaning tags here:

STAINS REMOVED: 0 1 2 3 4 5 6 7 8 9 10+

NUMBER OF TIMES I USUALLY WEAR THINGS BEFORE SENDING
TO THE CLEANERS: 0 1 2 3 4 5 6 7 8 9 10+

THINGS I MAY HAVE LEFT IN A POCKET:

_____

_____

Living in the moment

RIGHT NOW IT IS ___ : ___ A.M. / P.M.

I HEAR: _____

I SEE: _____

I FEEL:

□ HOT   □ COLD   □ JUST RIGHT   □ OTHER: _____

THOUGHTS OR LACK OF THOUGHTS:

REASONS LIVING IN THE MOMENT IS OVERRATED:

=== No. 37 ===

Magazines I saw at my last doctor's office visit:

☐ _____ ☐ _____
☐ _____ ☐ _____
☐ _____ ☐ _____
☐ _____ ☐ _____
☐ _____ ☐ _____
☐ _____ ☐ _____
☐ _____ ☐ _____
☐ _____ ☐ _____
☐ _____ ☐ _____
☐ _____ ☐ _____
☐ _____ ☐ _____
☐ _____ ☐ _____
☐ _____ ☐ _____
☐ _____ ☐ _____
☐ _____ ☐ _____
☐ _____ ☐ _____
☐ _____ ☐ _____

FREE SAMPLES I GOT
FROM THE DOCTOR:

OTHER PEOPLE'S AILMENTS
(CONFIRMED OR IMAGINED):

_____   _____

_____   _____

_____   _____

Train yourself
to recall old
memories while
you're sleeping.
Dreams are a
waste of time.

Times on the clock
I remember seeing today:

OTHER NUMBERS I REMEMBER SEEING TODAY: _ _ _ _ _ _ _ _ _ _ _ _

_ _

_ _

No.39

Memories of what I thought the future would be like when I was a kid:

FUTURE MEMORIES (INTERPRET HOWEVER):

No. 40

Cool T-shirts I saw last weekend:

I SAW THEM:

☐ ONLINE ☐ ON TV

☐ IN PUBLIC ☐ IN MY MIND

☐ OTHER: _____

No. 41

Place last strip of unused toilet paper from the roll here:

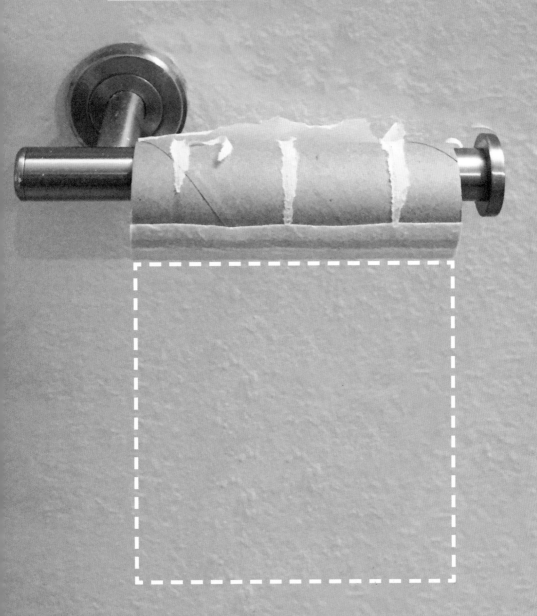

No. 42

All the childhood memories I can think of at the moment:

No.43

Place picture of a tourist attraction I've never been to here:

OTHER PLACES I SHOULD'VE VISITED BY NOW:

_____

_____

_____

_____

No. 44

Text messages I've written but didn't send:

(CHECK ALL THAT APPLY)

☐ 📷 | You broke my heart | | Send

☐ 📷 | How did you get this number | | Send

☐ 📷 | I am filled with rage at the moment | | Send

☐ 📷 | NO | | Send

☐ 📷 | ☹️ | | Send

☐ 📷 | I'm sorry | | Send

☐ 📷 | Fine | | Send

☐ 📷 | Call me | | Send

☐ 📷 | ?! | | Send

☐ 📷 | Let's do it! | | Send

☐ 📷 | ... | | Send

No. 45

First car I pulled up next to this morning:

TYPE OF CAR: _____

_____

_____

MUSIC COMING FROM THE CAR: _____

_____

_____

THE DRIVER LOOKED LIKE: _____

_____

_____

WORDS EXCHANGED: _____

_____

_____

DRIVER'S ASTROLOGICAL SIGN: _____

_____

_____

No.46

What I ate for lunch:

I ATE LUNCH AT: _____

WHAT I ATE:

DRAW WHAT SOMEONE ELSE WAS EATING HERE:

No. 47

Things on birthday wish lists I never received:

☐ _____
☐ _____
☐ _____
☐ _____
☐ _____
☐ _____
☐ _____
☐ _____

WORST BIRTHDAY EVER: _____
_____
_____

No.48

What I imagine that jerk from high school is up to right now:

(CHECK ALL THAT APPLY)

- ☐ WORKING AT A CONVENIENCE STORE

- ☐ PREGNANT WITH SEXTUPLETS

- ☐ IN JAIL IN SINGAPORE

- ☐ GOOGLING ME

- ☐ LIVING AT HOME

- ☐ SINGING SAD SONGS

- ☐ GETTING PUSHED INTO A POOL

- ☐ ABSOLUTELY NOTHING

- ☐ _____
  _____
  _____

J

NO. 49

Bathroom stall messages
I recently read:

No. 50

Things I recently wrote down somewhere else:

(BUT ALSO WANT TO WRITE HERE IN CASE ANYTHING
HAPPENS TO THE OTHER PLACES I WROTE THEM DOWN)

No.51

The names of everyone I've ever dated:

(OR "DATED")

- ☐ _____
- ☐ _____
- ☐ _____
- ☐ _____
- ☐ _____
- ☐ _____
- ☐ _____
- ☐ _____
- ☐ _____
- ☐ _____
- ☐ _____
- ☐ _____
- ☐ _____
- ☐ _____
- ☐ _____
- ☐ _____

MIDDLE NAMES OF EVERYONE I'VE EVER DATED:

_____
_____
_____
_____
_____

LEAST MEMORABLE DATE I'VE EVER BEEN ON:

_____
_____
_____
_____
_____

No. 52

The names of every teacher I can remember:

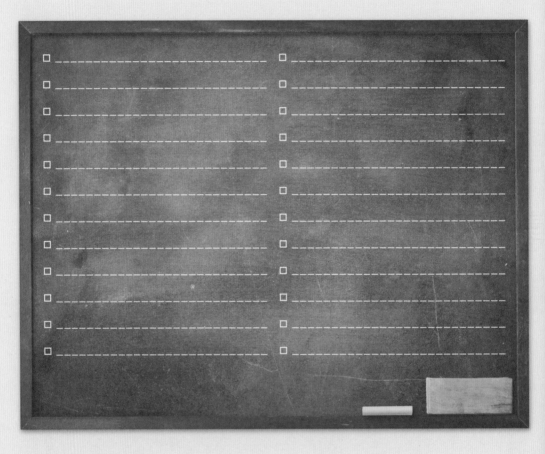

BEST LAB PARTNERS: _____

_____

WORST LAB PARTNERS: _____

_____

FAVORITE MATH EQUATION I'LL NEVER USE IN EVERYDAY LIFE:

_____

No. 53

The names of all my favorite TV lawyers:

VALUABLE LIFE LESSONS I'VE LEARNED FROM THEM:

IF I WAS A TV LAWYER, MY NAME WOULD BE _____ .

Repeat someone's name
15 times in your head
after they introduce
themselves. Names are
very important things
to remember.

No.54

A headline or news flash that caught my attention:

BREAKING NEWS BREAKING NEWS BREAKING NEWS BREAKING NEWS

_____

_____

_____

_____

_____

_____

_____

_____

A WORTHWHILE TIP I HALF-
HEARD IN A CONVERSATION
NEXT TO ME: _____

_____

_____

_____

_____

_____

_____

_____

GOOD BIT OF GOSSIP I
OVERHEARD ABOUT SOMEONE
I DON'T KNOW: _____

_____

_____

_____

_____

_____

_____

_____

No. 55

This morning's routine:

I WOKE UP AT: _____ A.M. / P.M. (CIRCLE ONE)

FIRST THOUGHT: _____

SONG I SANG IN THE SHOWER: _____

THOUGHTS WHILE BRUSHING MY TEETH:

_____

THIRD INGREDIENT LISTED IN MY TOOTHPASTE:

_____

FIRST FOOD I ATE (THAT DEFINITELY TASTED LIKE TOOTHPASTE):

_____

No.56

Bumper sticker sayings or designs I've noticed recently:

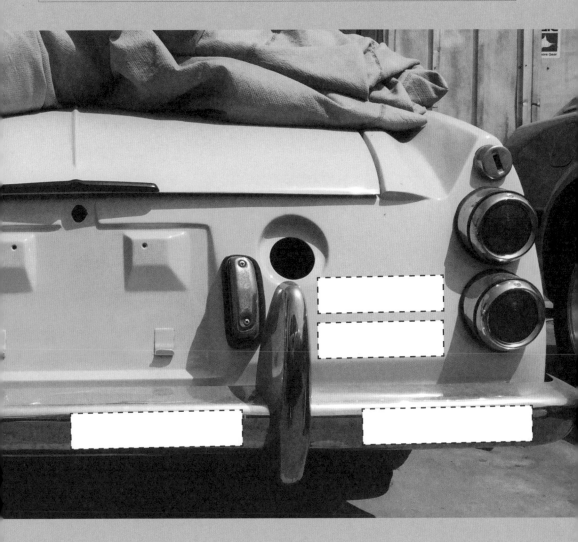

BUMPER STICKER SAYINGS TO REMEMBER: _____

BUMPER STICKERS I USED TO HAVE ON MY CAR: _____

_____

=== No.57 ===

My renditions of some tattoos I like but would never get:

No.58

Most embarrassing middle-school memories I can think of at the moment:

MEMORY LANE

No.59

Recap from a friend's recent vacation:

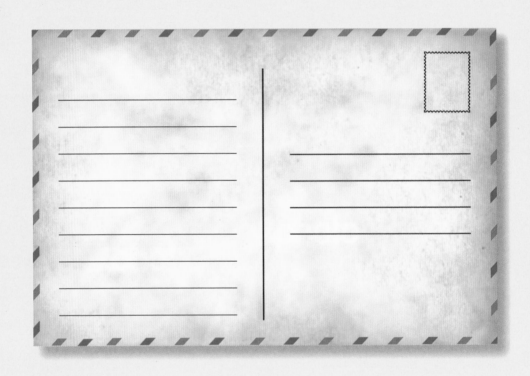

WHERE MY FRIEND WENT: _____

WHERE MY FRIEND STAYED: _____

LOCAL FOOD MY FRIEND TALKED ABOUT: _____

_____

_____

No. 60

Books I want to remember to read but probably won't:

- ☐ _____
- ☐ _____
- ☐ _____
- ☐ _____
- ☐ _____
- ☐ _____
- ☐ _____
- ☐ _____
- ☐ _____
- ☐ _____
- ☐ _____
- ☐ _____
- ☐ _____

BOOKS I'VE ALMOST BOUGHT:

- ☐ _____
- ☐ _____
- ☐ _____
- ☐ _____
- ☐ _____

No. 61

Favorite wireless password:

Network

Choose a security type and enter the name of the AirPort network to join with an optional password.

Network Name: [▼]

Wireless Security: [▲▼]

Password: [   ]

☑ Show password

(?)   (Cancel)   (OK)

MY EX'S WIRELESS PASSWORD:

_____

WIRELESS PASSWORDS AT COFFEE SHOPS I WENT TO ONCE:

_____

_____

_____

_____

_____

_____

Score from one of this week's sporting events:

SCORES FROM SPORTING EVENTS I REMEMBER FROM CHILDHOOD:

_____

_____

_____

_____

_____

_____

_____

No. 63

Place extra napkin, utensil, or menu from recent take-out order here:

WHAT I ORDERED:

_____

_____

_____

_____

ACTIVITY WHILE EATING:

_____

_____

_____

_____

No. 64

Clever vanity plates
I've seen lately:

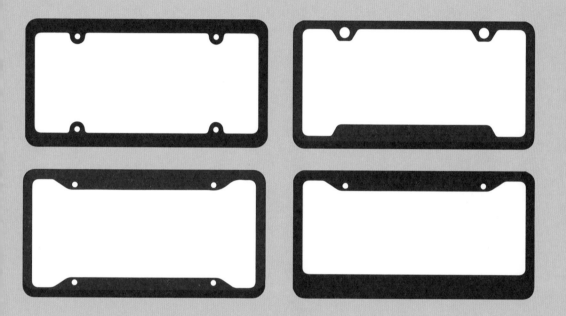

Keep all your receipts in a locked box under your bed. When one box fills up, buy another one. When you have no more room under your bed, rent a storage locker.

No. 65

Official names of
my past pets:

NICKNAMES OF MY PAST PETS: _____
_____
_____
_____

OTHER PETS I KNOW: _____
_____
_____

No. 66

Notes I got in school
I don't want to forget:

NOTES I'VE GOTTEN RECENTLY I DON'T
WANT TO FORGET:

DOCTOR'S NOTES I SHOULDN'T FORGET:

Weather report:

YESTERDAY'S FORECAST:

TOMORROW'S FORECAST:

NEXT WEDNESDAY'S FORECAST:

EMOTIONAL FORECAST:

No.68

Birthday gifts
I remember my
friends getting:

BIRTHDAY CAKE FLAVORS I REMEMBER FROM MY FRIENDS' PARTIES:

No. 69

Past bruises to remember:

(INCLUDE SHAPES AND SIZES)

_____
_____
_____
_____
_____
_____
_____
_____
_____
_____
_____
_____
_____
_____
_____
_____
_____

HOW I GOT THE BRUISES: _____
_____
_____
_____
_____

No. 70

People in magazines who look like people I know:

(PASTE PICTURES BELOW)

PERSON WHO REMINDS ME OF
MY FRIEND:

PERSON WHO REMINDS ME OF
MY BOSS:

PERSON WHO REMINDS ME OF
MY MOM:

PERSON WHO REMINDS ME OF
MY CHILDHOOD NEMESIS:

No. 71

TV episode titles to remember:

LOCAL TV NEWS STORIES I REMEMBER:

No.72

Place found notes I can't bear to part with here:

No. 73

Streets my friends live on:

STREETS I'VE SEEN ON VACATION:

STREETS I'VE SEEN IN MOVIES:

Living in the moment

CURRENT TIME:_____(A.M. / P.M.)

CURRENT THOUGHT (SHOULD BE NOTHING!):

CURRENT WISHES IF A GENIE SUDDENLY APPEARED:

CURRENT FEELINGS ABOUT GENIES:

—— NO.74 ——

What's right in
front of me:

WHAT'S PROBABLY RIGHT BEHIND ME: _____

_____

LIST OF EVERYTHING I NOTICE: _____

No.75

Trivia question
I heard recently:

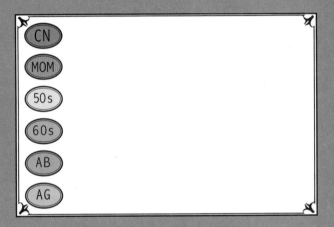

AN INCORRECT ANSWER I WAS SURE WAS CORRECT:

_____

_____

_____

_____

_____

CHILDHOOD MEMORY THE TRIVIA QUESTION TRIGGERED:

_____

_____

_____

_____

_____

Names of my friends' other friends:

- ☐ _____
- ☐ _____
- ☐ _____
- ☐ _____
- ☐ _____
- ☐ _____
- ☐ _____
- ☐ _____
- ☐ _____
- ☐ _____
- ☐ _____
- ☐ _____
- ☐ _____
- ☐ _____
- ☐ _____
- ☐ _____

- ☐ _____
- ☐ _____
- ☐ _____
- ☐ _____
- ☐ _____
- ☐ _____
- ☐ _____
- ☐ _____
- ☐ _____
- ☐ _____
- ☐ _____
- ☐ _____
- ☐ _____
- ☐ _____
- ☐ _____
- ☐ _____

NAMES OF MY FRIENDS' OLD CRUSHES:

_____

_____

NAMES OF FRIENDS' CAMP "BOYFRIENDS" AND/OR "GIRLFRIENDS":

_____

_____

No. 77

Memorable cupcakes:

(INCLUDE DATE, TIME, FLAVOR,
AND OTHER RELEVANT INFO)

MEMORABLE PANCAKES:

BAD CAKE MEMORIES (IF ANY):

No. 78

Recent sales calls
I've gotten:

WHAT I WAS DOING WHEN I GOT THE CALLS:

CALLER'S NAMES:

A FEW THINGS I LEARNED ABOUT THEM:

No. 79

Fundraising or charity opportunities I didn't take part in:

EXCUSES I USED:

THINGS I DID LATER OUT OF GUILT:

NO. 80

Bank account numbers from the receipts I just found at an ATM:

_____

_____

BALANCES (IF LISTED): _____

_____

_____

PASTE RECEIPTS HERE SO NO CRIMINALS GET THEIR HANDS ON THEM:

No. 81
Price of gas:

TODAY: $_____

LAST WEDNESDAY: $_____

PRICE OF BOTTLE OF WATER: $_____

PRICE OF FEATURED GAS STATION LIGHTERS: $_____

PRICE OF STRANGE MULTIVITAMINS: $_____

NAME ON ATTENDANT'S NAMETAG: _____

=== No.82 ===

Things that are currently in my pockets / pocketbook:

(CHECK ALL THAT APPLY)

☐ GUM

☐ KEYS

☐ WALLET

☐ LASER HAIR REMOVAL COUPONS

☐ PICTURES

☐ PLAYBILL FROM A FRIEND OF A FRIEND'S PLAY

☐ CHANGE

☐ INSPIRATIONAL QUOTES

☐

NO. 83

Types of cheese I can currently think of:

_____
_____
_____
_____
_____
_____
_____
_____
_____
_____

MY DAD'S FAVORITE KIND OF CHEESE:

_____

MY DENTIST'S FAVORITE KIND OF CHEESE:

_____

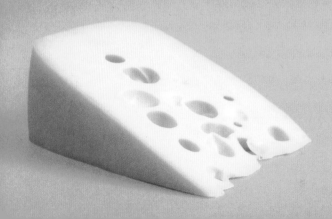

— No. 84 —

Grandma's gift corner:

(CIRCLE OR DRAW CHILDHOOD GIFTS FROM GRANDMA)

No. 85

Firsts in one word:

FIRST TIME SWIMMING:

_____

FIRST KISS:

_____

FIRST DAY OF SCHOOL:

_____

FIRST ACCIDENT:

_____

FIRST TIME EATING
AN AVOCADO:

_____

FIRST DMV EXPERIENCE:

_____

FIRST RELATIONSHIP:

_____

FIRST AIRPLANE RIDE:

_____

FIRST D-LIST
CELEBRITY CRUSH:

_____

= No.86 =

Draw and describe
a memorable meal:

No. 87

Driver's ed memories

WHAT I REMEMBER:

_____

_____

_____

WHAT MY PARENTS PROBABLY REMEMBER:

_____

_____

_____

WHAT MY TESTER PROBABLY REMEMBERS:

_____

_____

_____

DATE:

My most memorable Scantron test design:

(FROM WHEN I DIDN'T KNOW ANY OF THE ANSWERS TO A TEST)

	A B C D E		A B C D E		A B C D E
	A B C D E	26	A B C D E	51	A B C D E	76	A B C D E
	A B C D E	27	A B C D E	52	A B C D E	77	A B C D E
	A B C D E	28	A B C D E	53	A B C D E	78	A B C D E
	A B C D E	29	A B C D E	54	A B C D E	79	A B C D E
	A B C D E	30	A B C D E	55	A B C D E	80	A B C D E
	A B C D E	31	A B C D E	56	A B C D E	81	A B C D E
	A B C D E	32	A B C D E	57	A B C D E	82	A B C D E
	A B C D E	33	A B C D E	58	A B C D E	83	A B C D E
	A B C D E	34	A B C D E	59	A B C D E	84	A B C D E
	A B C D E	35	A B C D E	60	A B C D E	85	A B C D E
	A B C D E	36	A B C D E	61	A B C D E	86	A B C D E
	A B C D E	37	A B C D E	62	A B C D E	87	A B C D E
	A B C D E	38	A B C D E	63	A B C D E	88	A B C D E
	A B C D E	39	A B C D E	64	A B C D E	89	A B C D E
	A B C D E	40	A B C D E	65	A B C D E	90	A B C D E
	A B C D E	41	A B C D E	66	A B C D E	91	A B C D E
	A B C D E	42	A B C D E	67	A B C D E	92	A B C D E
	A B C D E	43	A B C D E	68	A B C D E	93	A B C D E
	A B C D E	44	A B C D E	69	A B C D E	94	A B C D E
	A B C D E	45	A B C D E	70	A B C D E	95	A B C D E
	A B C D E	46	A B C D E	71	A B C D E	96	A B C D E
	A B C D E	47	A B C D E	72	A B C D E	97	A B C D E
	A B C D E	48	A B C D E	73	A B C D E	98	A B C D E
	A B C D E	49	A B C D E	74	A B C D E	99	A B C D E
	A B C D E	50	A B C D E	75	A B C D E	100	A B C D E

—— No. 89 ——

The coolest person
I've ever seen in public:

WHAT I ASSUME THIS COOL PERSON DOES FOR WORK:

WHAT I ASSUME A DAY IN THIS COOL PERSON'S LIFE IS LIKE:

THINGS I ASSUME ABOUT THIS COOL PERSON'S SIGNIFICANT OTHER:

WHAT I ASSUME THIS COOL PERSON'S FAVORITE FOOD IS:

THE ONE THING I'LL NEVER FORGET ABOUT THE COOLEST PERSON:

No. 90

The scariest thing that's ever happened to me:

(WHEN CLEARLY NOTHING WAS WRONG)

_____

_____

_____

_____

_____

_____

_____

_____

_____

No. 91

A drawing of the perfect fort from my youth:

Don't go to sleep until you've written down a detailed description of your whole day. Every day is important!

THIS SPECIFIC JOURNAL MAY BE FILLED UP, BUT THAT DOESN'T MEAN YOU NEED TO GO BACK TO FORGETTING THINGS. EVERYTHING IS IMPORTANT AND WORTH REMEMBERING. WRITE DOWN YOUR BOSS'S PIZZA ORDER; YOU MAY NEED TO REMEMBER IT WHEN YOU'RE ORDERING HER A PIZZA. REMEMBER THE NAME OF THAT INN YOU DROVE PAST ON ROUTE 66; YOU COULD BE DRIVING DOWN ROUTE 66 ELEVEN YEARS FROM NOW AND NEED A PLACE TO STAY! WRITE EVERYTHING DOWN ALL THE TIME AND YOU'LL NEVER HAVE TO WORRY ABOUT ANYTHING EVER AGAIN.